Piano Exam Pieces

ABRSM Grade 8

Selected from the 2017 & 2018 syllabus

Name

Date of exam

D0237560

Contents

Editor for ABRSM: Richard Jones

Other pieces for Grade 8

First published in 2016 by ABRSM (Publishing) Ltd,
a wholly owned subsidiary of ABRSM, 24 Portland Place,
London W1B 1LU, United Kingdom
© 2016 by The Associated Board of the Royal Schools of Music
Distributed worldwide by Oxford University Press

Music origination by Julia Bovee
Cover by Kate Benjamin & Andy Potts
Printed in England by Halstan & Co. Ltd, Amersham,
Bucks., on materials from sustainable sources.
Reprinted in 2016

A:1

Gigue

Seventh movement from French Suite No. 5 in G, BWV 816

J. S. Bach
(1685–1750)

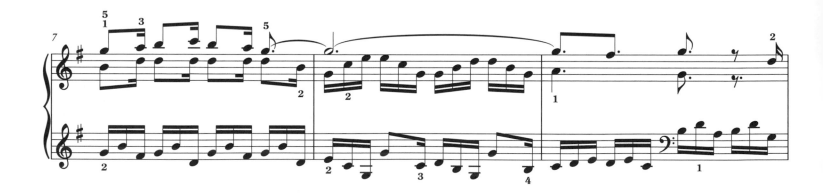

All but the last of Bach's six French Suites were dedicated to his highly musical young wife Anna Magdalena. They form the opening items in her *Clavierbüchlein* (Little Keyboard Book) of 1722, though Suite No. 5 in G, from which this Gigue is selected, was not completed till 1724 – after the family's move from Cöthen to Leipzig. From that year onwards Bach made much use of the six suites for teaching purposes.

As often in Bach, the Gigue is designed as a three-part fugue in typical gigue rhythm, built into an overall binary dance form. The exposition (bb. 1–9) presents three entries of the playful, vivacious subject (treble, middle, bass), combined with two countersubjects (bb. 7–9, RH). The remainder of the first half consists of motivic episodes interspersed with two subject entries in the dominant key D (bb. 14 and 20). The second half is built on a free inversion of the subject, which now enters in the opposite order (bass, middle, treble; bb. 25–35), combined with a new, highly characterful countersubject (b. 28, bass). A brief episode leads to a second rising series of entries, modulating downwards through the circle of 5ths: e – a – D – G (bb. 39, 44, 46, 49). The movement concludes with a low tonic bass entry (b. 52) plus a brief coda.

Sources: autograph MS and pupils' copies, Staatsbibliothek zu Berlin, Preußischer Kulturbesitz, Mus.ms.Bach P 224, P 420 and P 1221; Washington, Library of Congress, ML96.B187

A:2

Fugue in B flat

HWV 607

No. 3 from *Six Fugues or Voluntarys*

G. F. Handel
(1685–1759)

This is Handel's keyboard transcription of an orchestral fugue from the Sinfonia to his *Brockes Passion* of 1715. The keyboard version probably dates from 1717/18, when Handel lived in London, under the patronage of the Duke of Chandos. In 1735 it was published alongside other fugues from the Cannons years under the title *Six Fugues or Voluntarys for the Organ or Harpsicord* [*sic*].

This piece is a double fugue in which the main subject is combined with a second subject of almost equal importance. Stretto treatment (overlapping entries) of S I (first subject) and imitative/sequential treatment of S II (second subject) form the main substance of the fugue, and they are already anticipated in the opening exposition (bb. 3–4 and 5–10 respectively). This exposition (bb. 1–17) contains three entries of S I in the order treble, middle, bass – each combined with S II – plus an additional entry in the middle part (b. 14). The modulatory middle section contains four expositions in various keys, each opening with a stretto on S I (bb. 25, 35, 46 and 53). The linking episodes are based largely on S II. A final, climactic tonic entry of S I + II in the outer parts (b. 65) leads into a coda built on the main figure of S II (b. 68). 'Adagio' in the closing bars – as usual in the music of the period – may be taken to mean *allargando*.

Sources: autograph MS, British Library, R.M. 20.g.14; *Six Fugues or Voluntarys for the Organ or Harpsicord* [*sic*], Op. 3 (London: J. Walsh, 1735)

Adapted from Handel: *Selected Keyboard Works*, Book IV, edited by Richard Jones (ABRSM)

8

A:3

Prelude and Fugue in A minor

No. 2 from 24 Preludes and Fugues

R. K. Shchedrin
(born 1932)

The Russian composer and pianist Rodion Shchedrin studied at the Moscow Conservatory (1951–5), where he later taught composition (1965–9). His early music owed much to Prokofiev, but his later compositions are more advanced in style and technique, adopting serial and avant-garde procedures. The diverse influences on his music include Russian folksong and the works of J. S. Bach – hence Shchedrin's *Musical Offering*, *Echo Sonata* for solo violin, and *Polyphonic Notebook*. A further Bach tribute is the collection of 24 preludes and fugues for piano (1964–70), from which this pair of movements is selected.

The Prelude is a brilliant toccata in A minor, highly symmetrical in form, consisting of four 16-bar periods (the musical equivalent of sentences; bb. 1, 17, 33 and 49), each made up of two eight-bar phrases. Although the composer's metronome mark is ♩ = 88–92, students might prefer a slower tempo, for example ♩ = *c*.80.

The following three-part Fugue, built on a highly expressive, chromatic subject, falls into four expositions (bb. 1, 14, 28 and 43), each of which closes with the same very distinctive codetta and cadence bar (see bb. 11–13). The first exposition, in the tonic A minor, presents the subject entries in the order treble, bass, middle part.

The three following expositions are all based on the principle of stretto (overlapping entries). The second exposition (b. 14) presents two strettos (both in the order bass, treble, middle part) – the first based on the direct subject only; the second, on the inverted subject (bass, middle), combined with its direct form (treble). The third exposition (b. 28) opens with a stretto in which retrograde (reversed) entries in the middle and treble parts are combined with an inverted entry in the bass. Then the inverted subject is heard twice in the treble – first hand-crossed to the bottom of the texture (b. 33), then back at the top (b. 37), combined with a retrograde inversion in the bass.

The conclusion comes with the fourth and last exposition (b. 43), in which constant reiterations of the subject's repeated-note motive form lengthy pedal points (bb. 43–60). Meanwhile, two concluding strettos on the direct subject are heard at bb. 44 (treble, bass, middle) and 50 (bass and treble only).

AB 3820

Prelude

Vivace ♩. = 88–92

Fugue

Moderato ♩ = 100

B:1

Rondo

Third movement from Sonata in E, Op. 14 No. 1

Edited by Barry Cooper

Ludwig van Beethoven
(1770–1827)

Beethoven's two piano sonatas Op. 14 were probably both composed in 1798 and were published in the following year. They belong to his early period in Vienna (1792–1802), when he played regularly in the homes of the Viennese aristocracy and established an enviable reputation as a brilliant young pianist and composer. His patrons at that time included Baroness Josephine von Braun, to whom the Op. 14 sonatas were dedicated. According to William Kinderman (*Beethoven*, Oxford, 1995), 'the impact of Mozart is felt in several of Beethoven's piano sonatas of these [early] years, including…the two sonatas of Op. 14.'

The finale of the E major Sonata, selected here, is composed in sonata-rondo form, but with a reprise of the B-section in the subdominant rather than in the more usual tonic. The overall form is: A (b. 1, key I), B (b. 21, V), A^1 (b. 30, I, modulating), C (b. 47, mod.), A^2 (b. 83, I–IV), B^1 (b. 98, IV, mod.), A^3 (b. 108, I). In the central C-section, the staccatos need to be well-marked and emphatic to characterize the energetic rhythm of the theme. For further advice on interpretation, see the commentary (p. 56) to Barry Cooper's ABRSM edition. In b. 97, treble, only the semiquaver pairs are slurred; slurring has been corrected according to b. 20. The edition printed here has broken slur lines to indicate editorial extensions of existing slurs.

Source: first edition, *Deux sonates pour le piano-forte*, Op. 14 (Vienna: T. Mollo, [1799])

Allegro

First movement from Sonata in C, K. 279

W. A. Mozart
(1756–91)

The Sonata in C, K. 279, from which this Allegro has been selected, is the first of a set of six piano sonatas – Mozart's earliest surviving contributions to the genre – written while the 19-year-old composer was staying in Munich in early 1775. The set might have been intended for publication, but only one of the six sonatas was published during Mozart's lifetime. In 1777 he wrote to his father Leopold from Augsburg: 'Here and at Munich I have played all my six sonatas [in public] by heart several times.'

The autograph MS of the six sonatas, K. 279–84, starts with the second movement of K. 279; the first movement was apparently lost in the late 19th century. The text used for this edition consequently follows an early edition that was evidently based on the lost autograph. Dynamics are sparse in the first 12 bars and occasionally elsewhere, and have been supplemented by editorial suggestions. The right-hand *f* in bb. 12 and 13 is equivalent to *sf*. The bass crotchet at the start of bb. 68 and 69 has been corrected by the editor to quaver plus quaver rest in accordance with bb. 13 and 14. In bb. 76–7, the *f* signs do not occur in the source till the first half of b. 77, but they are surely misplaced (cf. b. 80).

Source: Mozart: *Billigste und correcte Original Ausgabe Sonaten für Pianoforte allein* (Offenbach: Johann André, [1841])

B:3

Presto

First movement from Sonata in E minor, Hob. XVI:34

Joseph Haydn
(1732–1809)

Until the late 1770s Haydn was obliged by contract to compose exclusively for his employer Prince Nikolaus Esterházy, unless granted special permission to do otherwise. In 1779, however, the prince released him from this obligation. His music was then published in Paris and London as well as in Vienna, and by the early 1780s he had become one of the most celebrated composers in Europe. This reputation rested largely on his symphonies and string quartets, but it is now widely recognized that his piano sonatas are of comparable importance.

Haydn composed over 60 sonatas during a period of roughly 35 years (*c*.1761–95). The earlier sonatas were written for the harpsichord, but during the years 1783–95 he published ten sonatas for the fortepiano; and these, alongside Mozart's sonatas of the 1780s, represent the culmination of the Viennese Classical style of keyboard music. To this late group belongs the Sonata in E minor, Hob. XVI:34, which was composed in about 1783 and first published in London in the following year. The first movement, selected here, shows the mature Haydn at his most passionate. The musical argument turns on the contrast between the quietly lyrical opening theme in the tonic E minor and the stormy reply in the relative major G (b. 14). Sources: MS copy, Graz, Steiermärkisches Landesarchiv, Sign. 40975, Karton 316; first edition, *A Fifth Sett [sic.] of Sonatas for the Piano Forte or Harpsichord* (London: Beardmore & Birchall, [1784])

C:1

Adriana

No. 1 from *Valses venezolanos*

Miguel Astor
(born 1958)

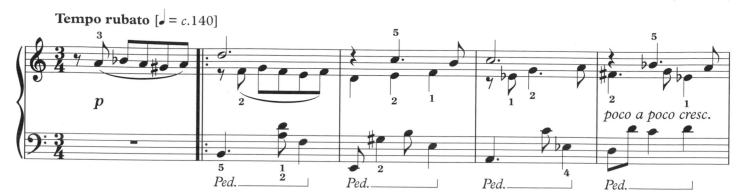

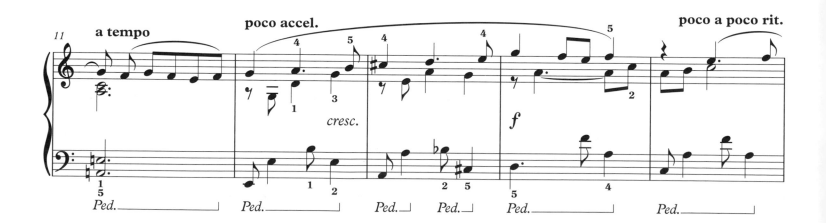

The Venezuelan composer Miguel Astor studied at the Central University, Caracas, and at the National Conservatory of Music in the same city. He is now a professor at the Department of Musicology in the Central University and also at the National University of Experimental Arts. His piano works include two sonatas, four Venezuelan suites, *El piano multimodal*, which contains 12 fugues written in homage to J. S. Bach, and *Valses venezolanos* (Venezuelan Waltzes), of which 'Adriana' is the first.

'Adriana', composed in 1987, is nostalgic in character, with a contrasting central section – faster and more cheerful – in which the left-hand rhythmic figure is reminiscent of the traditional Venezuelan waltz accompaniment. National elements of this kind are combined with rich, pungent harmonies that owe much to jazz.

Intermezzo in A minor

No. 7 from *Clavierstücke*, Op. 76

C:2

Johannes Brahms
(1833–97)

During his later years, between 1879 and 1893, Brahms published six sets of relatively short, lyrical piano pieces (Opp. 76, 79 and 116–19), chiefly under the non-committal titles of Intermezzo, Capriccio and Rhapsody. The eight pieces of Op. 76 were completed in 1878 during his summer visit to the south Austrian resort of Pörtschach am Wörthersee (by Lake Wörther). As often, beautiful surroundings seem to have encouraged his creativity.

The A minor Intermezzo is cast in an overall frame form – the opening rather formal 8-bar period (the musical equivalent to a sentence) acts as both introduction and conclusion. The main content of the piece (bb. 8–37), romantic and deeply expressive, is cast in rounded binary form **with repeats that should be observed in the exam**. Note that the right-hand melody at bb. 16b–18 is imitated by the left hand at bb. 18 (second half) to 20. In bb. 34b–37 the melody line shifts to the alto part.

Source: *Clavierstücke*, Op. 76 (Berlin: N. Simrock, 1879); Brahms's *Handexemplar*, with autograph corrections, Vienna, Gesellschaft der Musikfreunde

©1988 by The Associated Board of the Royal Schools of Music
Adapted from Brahms: *Eight Piano Pieces*, Op. 76, edited by Howard Ferguson (ABRSM)

卖杂货 Mai Za Huo

Selling Sundry Goods

No. 1 from *Four Piano Pieces based on Cantonese Melodies*, Op. 5

Peixun Chen
(1921–2006)

C:3

The Chinese composer Peixun Chen was born in Hong Kong and studied composition at the National Conservatory of Music in Shanghai (1939–41). In 1949 he became a founder-member of the Central Conservatory of Music, Beijing, where he taught composition and orchestration. He returned to his native Hong Kong in 1980, teaching at the Baptist College there till his retirement in 1986.

Chen often made use of Cantonese folk tunes in his music. Some of his arrangements of these have become very popular in China, including 'Selling Sundry Goods' (1952), which is from his collection *Four Piano Pieces based on Cantonese Melodies* (广东音乐主题钢琴曲四首 Guangdong Yin Yue Zhu Ti Gang Qin Qu Si Shou). 'Selling Sundry Goods' falls into the ternary form ABA[1]: the A-sections (bb. 1 and 64) present and vary the Cantonese folk tune of the title – the song of a pedlar selling his wares – and the more lyrical B-section (b. 41) is based on another folk melody, *The Dressing Table*, from the same region of southern China. Note the canonic writing between the hands in bb. 50–61.

Allegretto [tempo primo]

Allegro ♩ = c.120

C:4

Jazzy

No. 3 from *Three Moods*

Aaron Copland
(1900–90)

Aaron Copland, one of the outstanding American composers of the 20th century, took a strong interest in jazz from an early age and, using its influence, forged a distinctively American style of composition. His *Three Moods* of 1920–1 were first performed by Copland himself in Paris in September 1921. Subsequently, he played No. 3, 'Jazzy', to the well-known French composition teacher Nadia Boulanger, who on hearing the piece accepted him as a composition student. Although the composer's metronome mark for the outer sections is ♩ = 84, they might be played at a more relaxed tempo, for example ♩ = *c.*76. Candidates may interpret the ♫ figures as swung quavers at their discretion, as many performers of this piece choose to do.

Doctor Gradus ad Parnassum

C:5

No. 1 from *Children's Corner*

Claude Debussy
(1862–1918)

Claude Debussy, perhaps the most influential French composer of the late 19th century and 20th century, studied piano, theory and composition at the Paris Conservatoire from 1872 to 1884. As winner of the *Prix de Rome*, a much coveted composition prize, he travelled to Rome and stayed there from 1885 to 1887. He often toured England, Russia, and other European countries, performing his own music as conductor and pianist.

Debussy's mature piano music is regarded by many as the most original contribution to the repertory since Chopin. His piano suite *Children's Corner* was published in 1908 with a dedication 'à ma chère petite Chouchou' (to my dear little Chouchou), the nickname of his three-year-old daughter Claude-Emma. Although the music is as advanced and sophisticated as anything in Debussy's oeuvre, the titles of the six pieces refer to various objects in the child's world – dolls, a toy elephant, snow, a little shepherd. However, the first piece, selected here, refers to the piano études that the little girl would have heard in her home. The title alludes to Clementi's collection of studies *Gradus ad Parnassum*. Debussy translates the earlier composer's étude style into his own impressionist idiom, breathing into it the aesthetic beauty and strength of feeling of a great work of art. Source: *Children's Corner (Coin des enfants). Petite Suite pour piano seul* (Paris: Durand, 1908).

un peu retenu

a tempo

m.g. [LH] *expressif*

C:6

Allegro

First movement from Sonatina No. 3, Op. 41

Lars-Erik Larsson
(1908–86)

The Swedish composer Lars-Erik Larsson studied at the Stockholm Conservatory (now the Royal College of Music in Stockholm) (1925–9), and then undertook further studies in Vienna with Alban Berg and in Leipzig (1929–30). He was employed by Swedish Radio as a conductor, composer and producer (1937–53) and, during the same period, became professor of composition at Stockholm Conservatory (1947–59) and later music director at Uppsala University (1961–6). His creative work is eclectic, drawing styles and techniques from a variety of sources, including late romanticism, neo-classicism, serialism and polytonality.

This Allegro from Larsson's Sonatina No. 3, Op. 41 (1950), may be understood as being in sonata form. Theme A (bb. 1–20) – a running theme in octaves, answered by cross-rhythm chords – contrasts markedly with the tender, bitter-sweet theme B (bb. 20–34), with its simultaneous major and minor 3rds. During the development (bb. 35–75), variants of the two themes are presented in alternation. The recapitulation (bb. 76–94) is devoted to theme A only – first in its climactic variant form from the start of the development (b. 76 = b. 35), and then in its original form (b. 86 = b. 1), abridged and brought to a close by a striking cadence drawn from bb. 14–15.

58